Reading
Comprehension
Grade 2

Read · Think · Learn

- Read each section carefully.

- Be sure to also review the illustrations.

- You may review as needed to answer the questions at the end of each section.

- Compare and Connect: Some questions will ask you to compare details or information from two or more sections, so be sure to read the sections in order.

Illustrated by John Jordan

© 2016 Bendon, Inc. All rights reserved.
The BENDON name and logo are trademarks
of Bendon, Inc., Ashland, OH 44805.

Read carefully. Then answer the questions.

Animals of the African Savanna

The wild animals of Africa are amazing! Many live on the grassy savanna, where it is hot most of the time. There are not many trees on the savanna. Animals must blend in with the grass and bushes to hide—or they must run very fast!

African Elephant

The African elephant is the largest land animal in the world. The males are called bulls. The females are called cows. The large African bull elephants can weigh more than 12,000 pounds. That's as much as 60 men! Elephants live in groups called herds. The babies are called calves.

African elephants have very large ears and a long trunk. An elephant uses its trunk to suck up water, squirt itself to cool off, and reach the leaves of tall trees.

African Rhinoceros

The African rhinoceros is a huge, fast animal. It eats grass, twigs, leaves, and fruit. When it gets hot on the African savanna, the rhino takes a cool mud bath.

The rhino doesn't see well, but it does have a big, sharp horn to protect itself. The rhino's horn can grow to three feet long. It is not made of bone. It's made of *keratin* (fibers like those in your hair and fingernails).

Giraffe

The giraffe is the tallest animal in the world. The males can grow to more than 17 feet tall. That's about three men high! Giraffes eat leaves, which they can reach with their l-o-n-g neck and long tongue.

The giraffe spends its whole life on its feet. When it sleeps, it bends its neck, touching the ground with its head.

African Lion

The African lion is the largest, strongest cat in Africa. It is called the king of beasts. The male lion has a full, thick mane, unlike other large cats around the world. Lions live in groups called prides. Baby lions are called cubs.

Lions hunt animals for food. They often hunt at night when it is cool. In the daytime, lions may nap on tree branches or rest near water. Male lions sleep about 20 hours a day.

Gnu (Wildebeest)

This odd-looking animal is a gnu (pronounced "new") or wildebeest (**will-da-beast**). Gnus live in huge herds—up to 200,000! They are often hunted by lions and other animals. They stay together, moving from one grassy feeding area to the next. Gnus must stay on the move. They can go without water for five days.

Answer the questions.
Refer back to the text and pictures as needed.

1. The African savanna is
   a. wet and cold
   b. grassy and warm
   c. filled with trees
   d. rocky and dry

2. What is a female elephant called?

_____

3. The horn of a rhinoceros is made of
   a. bone
   b. ivory
   c. keratin
   d. wood

4. What is taller, a bull elephant or a giraffe?

_____

5. How is a male African lion different from other big cats?

_____

What do you think?

6. Do you think gnus would rather be around giraffes or lions? Why?

_____

_____

Read carefully. Then answer the questions.

South American Rain Forest

The Amazon rain forest of South America is the largest rain forest in the world. It is home to many strange and beautiful animals. They live on the ground and up in the trees—even in the tops of the tallest trees.

Macaw

The Amazon rain forest is filled with beautiful birds. The macaws are the largest parrots in the Americas. They come in many colors, from deep reds and greens to bright blues. When they gather in the treetops they can be quite a noisy group.

Macaws use their strong beaks and toes to help them move from branch to branch. Their big beaks are very good at cracking open nuts, large seeds, and snail shells.

Howler Monkey

The rain forest is home to many kinds of monkeys. Spider monkeys and little squirrel monkeys swing through the treetops.

The howler is the biggest monkey in the Americas. It can weigh up to 20 pounds. This monkey screams, or howls, to say "This is my land!" The screams are so loud, they can be heard as far as three miles away! The howler monkey likes to stay in trees, moving from branch to branch.

Sloth

The sloth is a strange animal. It is about two feet long and hangs upside down from trees with its huge claws. It sleeps about 15 hours a day and moves s-l-o-w-l-y from branch to branch in search of leaves and buds to eat.

Adult sloths sometimes look like they have green fur. The green comes from *bacteria* (back-**teer**-ee-ah) that grow on their fur. A sloth's thick, green fur can even be home to small insects. So, a sloth is sort of a small forest living in the forest!

Jaguar

The jaguar is the largest cat in the Americas. It has long teeth and sharp claws. These big cats move quietly through the forest on their big, padded paws. They look for small mammals, reptiles, and eggs to eat. They are good tree climbers and excellent swimmers.

Jaguars have beautiful spotted coats that help them blend in with the light and shadows of the rain forest. Every jaguar has its own pattern of spots.

Answer the questions.
Refer back to the text and pictures as needed.

1. How is a macaw's beak useful?

_____

_____

_____

2. Is a baby sloth born with green fur?

_____

3. Which could be found in a tree in the rain forest?
   a. macaw
   b. sloth
   c. jaguar
   d. all of these

4. Name two animals in the South American rain forest that are very noisy or loud.

_____

_____

5. Can an animal always escape a jaguar by crossing over a river? Why or why not?

_____

_____

Illustration Research

6. Baby sloths and baby howler monkeys cling and ride along with their mothers, but they ride differently. What is the difference?

_____

_____

_____

What do you think?

7. Would it be easier to see a macaw or a sloth in the treetops? Why?

_____

_____

Compare and Connect

8. How does the savanna look different from the rain forest?

_____

_____

9. Which sleeps more: a sloth or a male African lion?

_____

Read carefully. Then answer the questions.

Animals of Australia

Australia is filled with animals that are very, very different from animals in other lands. There are many interesting birds, mammals, reptiles, and *marsupials* (mar-**soo**-pee-uhls). A marsupial is a mammal that carries its baby in a pouch on its body.

19

Red Kangaroo

Red kangaroos are the world's biggest marsupials. When the red kangaroo stands up, it's taller than a man! Red kangaroos live in dry areas and eat plants and grass. Those long legs help them make great leaps! "Big reds" can "long jump" up to 17 feet!

A baby kangaroo is called a joey. A newborn joey is pink with no hair. It lives in its mother's pouch until it can hop about on its own.

Koala

The koala looks like a teddy, but it's a marsupial—*not* a bear! It has very strong, sharp toenails that cling tightly to branches. Koalas only eat *eucalyptus* (you-kuh-**lip**-tus) leaves, so they live in only a few places.

A baby koala is also called a joey. A newborn joey is about the size of a lima bean. It lives in its mother's pouch for about six months. Young joeys then ride around on their mother's back.

Coral Reef

Australia has incredible coral reefs, which are underwater areas where many plants, fish, and other animals live. Different kinds of coral create a reef—some shaped like trees, others like flowers, and some even look like big brains!

Corals are not plants. They are hard, shell-like skeletons formed by tiny jellylike animals, called *polyps* (**paul**-ips), that live inside the hard skeletons.

Sea *anemones* (uh-**nem**-uh-neez) are lovely reef animals. Some are small, no bigger than a grape. Others can be six feet wide. The orange-and-white clownfish can hide in the "petals" of the sea anemone, but those petals can sting and poison other animals.

The sea horse has a strange shape for a fish. Its tail winds around water plants to hold it in place. To move, the little sea horse beats the fanlike fin on its back.

Crocodile

Australia is also home to the saltwater crocodile. It can grow to 30 feet long! It lives in rivers and swamps. It can also swim from island to island in saltwater. It is sometimes called a "saltie."

This huge croc eats fish, crabs, and mammals—even big mammals. It can leap at them—from right out of the water! Stay away!

Sharks

The waters off the coast of Australia are rich with fish. The largest fish are the sharks. Sharks are good hunters with rows and rows of sharp teeth in their huge mouths.

Most fish have bones, but sharks do not. A shark's skeleton is made of *cartilage* (**car-tih-lidge**) like the cartilage that forms the ears on your head. This means that a shark is "rubbery" and able to twist and turn easily.

> Answer the questions.
> Refer back to the text and pictures as needed.

1. Which statement is NOT true?
   a. Big reds are the biggest marsupials.
   b. Big reds can jump 10 feet.
   c. Big reds eat plants.
   d. Big reds live in the rain forest.

2. Is a koala a kind of bear?

_____

3. The living things inside coral are
   a. jellylike animals   c. little fish
   b. jellylike plants   d. small flowers

4. What kind of fish can hide in a sea anemone?

_____

5. A sea horse is a kind of
   a. sea mammal   c. fish
   b. shrimp   d. sea lizard

6. A saltie is a kind of
   a. shark   c. coral
   b. crocodile   d. marsupial

7. Why are sharks able to twist and turn easily?

_____

_____

8. Name two animals that have babies called joeys.

_____

_____

Illustration Research

9. Look at the pictures of the howler monkey and the sea horse. What can they both do?

_____

_____

What do you think?

10. Could a koala harm a person? With what?

_____

_____

Animals of Southern Asia

The lands of southern Asia are warm and often rainy and wet. In the jungles and forests here, monkeys scamper from tree to tree. Colorful birds fly in the air. The drier, open, grassy areas are called the savanna. Animals may *migrate* (move with the seasons) between the forest and the savanna.

One of the most handsome animals of the savanna is the Bengal tiger. It is known as the "royal tiger." Males are about ten feet long and can weigh up to 600 pounds!

Asian Elephant

Asian elephants can weigh 10,000 pounds. They eat 200 pounds of grass and leaves a day. Only a few males (and no females) have tusks.

Asian elephants are large, but they can be gentle and easily tamed. Elephants are intelligent animals. They have been trained to do work, such as move heavy logs or carry people. An elephant may work its whole life with one driver, called a *mahout* (muh-**howt**).

Python

The python is a large snake that lives in the jungles and forests of southern Asia. Pythons can grow to be 20 feet long. The python is a *constrictor*. It wraps around and strangles its *prey* (animal it eats).

Pythons are excellent climbers. Some live in trees. A python may rest on a branch for quite a while waiting for a meal to come by. That's fine with a python. It can go a long time between meals—up to a year!

Proboscis Monkey

The proboscis (pro-**boss**-kiss) monkey gets its name from the male's big nose. A proboscis is a long snout or nose. The large nose helps make the monkey's screams even louder. Females are smaller than males, but both have tails as long as their bodies.

These friendly Asian monkeys live along the coast or near riverbanks. They eat leaves, fruit, and flowers. They spend most of their time in trees, but they are also great swimmers.

Orangutan

Orangutans (oh-**rang**-oo-tans) of Asia are large, clever apes that live most of their lives in trees. They use their long, strong arms to swing from one tree to another without touching the ground. Their name means "man of the forest."

Orangutans eat fruit, leaves, small animals, and eggs. Mothers have only one baby at a time. They look after each baby for six or seven years.

Answer the questions.
Refer back to the text and pictures as needed.

1. Name a big cat that lives in southern Asia.

_____

2. Do female Asian elephants have tusks?

_____

3. Which statement is NOT true?
   a. Pythons eat tree leaves.
   b. Pythons are constrictors.
   c. Pythons can climb trees.
   d. Pythons are large snakes.

4. What is odd about a male proboscis monkey?

_____

5. What does "orangutan" mean?

_____

6. An orangutan is an ape. Apes do not have tails. Is a proboscis monkey also an ape?

_____

7. What does *mahout* mean?
   a. snout
   b. driver
   c. move with the seasons
   d. food animal

Illustration Research

8. Look at the pictures of the African and the Asian elephants. What is the main difference between the two?

_____

_____

9. Look at the pictures of the South American jaguar and the Bengal tiger. How are they different?

_____

_____

Compare and Connect

10. Fill in the blanks with names of continents.

The savanna of southern Asia is like the

grassy area of _____. The jungles

of southern Asia are wet and warm like the

rain forest of _____.

Animals of North America

North America is home to a many wild animals. In the cold north there are snow hares, wolves, and moose.

In the mountains and forests there are deer, squirrels, foxes, and bears. Bison and prairie dogs live on the great, wide, grassy lands called the plains. Alligators and water birds can be found in some of the wetlands. Lizards, snakes, and cougars live in rocky areas and dry deserts.

Black Bear

The American black bear lives in the forests of North America. Black bears stand about as tall as a man and weigh 200 to 600 pounds. They eat fruit, nuts, roots, fish, and grubs. They also like camp grub! People often see black bears in camping areas. Bears come into the camp when they smell food cooking.

Little bear cubs are cute, but you should never go up to one. A mother bear will attack anyone who goes near her cub!

Bighorn Sheep

The bighorn is a wild sheep that lives on mountain cliffs and dry *plateaus* (pla-**toes**), which are high, flat areas. It feeds on grass, roots, buds, and bark. The rams (males) have curved horns that can grow to two feet long and weigh 25 pounds. Each ring on the horns shows one year of growth.

At one time there were very few bighorn sheep left in the wild. With the help of the Boy Scouts, new laws were made to save these handsome animals.

Gray Wolf

Gray wolves used to live all over North America. Today wolves live in Canada and Alaska, and some have been brought back to the northern parts of the United States.

Gray wolves can run all night with little rest. They are also good swimmers. By working together in a pack, wolves bring down large prey, such as deer. However, wolves mainly eat smaller prey, such as rats, rabbits, and squirrels.

Cougar

The cougar (**koo**-ger) is also called a puma (**poo**-mah), mountain lion, and panther. This big cat lives in the cold mountains of Canada and in the deserts and forests of the United States and Mexico. Cougars are excellent hunters. They prey on mice, small mammals, and birds.

A cougar can act just like a really big pet cat. It washes its face with a paw, rolls onto its back, and eats like a house cat. But, no matter how cute these cats may look, they can never be pets. These big cats are wild!

Rattlesnake

Most snakes in North America are not harmful to people. Some, however, like rattlesnakes, bite with sharp fangs and inject a *venom* (**ven**-um) that stuns or kills their prey.

Rattlesnakes live in forests and deserts across North America. They have thick bodies, but they are fast. They hunt small mammals and birds, but will strike at anything that bothers them. This snake's rattling tail is a warning to stay back! The rattle is made of dry scales left over each time the snake *molts* (sheds its skin).

Bald Eagle

The bald eagle is the national bird of the United States. It is a large bird with a seven-foot wingspan. It has sharp eyesight and can spot prey from high up on a tree branch. It then swoops down and grabs a small mammal or fish in its *talons* (claws).

The male and female eagle build a large nest called an *aerie* (**air**-ee) in the branches of a tall tree or on a cliff. They take turns hunting and caring for their eaglets.

43

> Answer the questions.
> Refer back to the text and pictures as needed.

1. The grassy lands of Africa are called the savanna. What are they called in North America?

   _____

2. Black Bears like camp grub. Camp grub is
   a. campfire logs   c. camp food
   b. camp sounds   d. camp bugs

3. How can you tell how old a bighorn ram is?

   _____

   _____

4. In what state could you see a gray wolf in the wild?
   a. Mississippi   c. Kansas
   b. Florida   d. Alaska

5. List three other names for a cougar.

   _____

   _____

   _____

6. A rattlesnake's rattle is made of
   a. bone pieces   c. keratin
   b. dry scales   d. cartilage

7. What is longer: a bald eagle's wing or a bighorn sheep's horn?

What do you think?

8. Where could you find a puma: on a plateau or an aerie?

Compare and Connect

9. Draw a line from each animal to her babies.

   elephant   cubs
   eagle   joeys
   koala   calves
   bear   eaglets

10. What is different about the way pythons and rattlesnakes kill their prey?

Answer Pages

Note: Some answers may vary depending upon your own thoughts, example, or wording. These answers serve as guides.

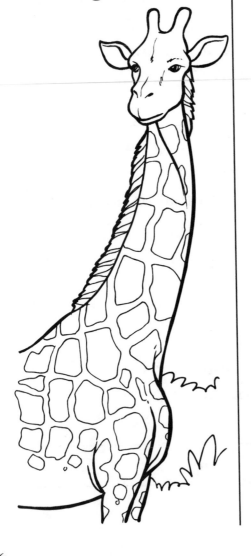

Animals of the African Savanna
page 9

1. b. grassy and warm
2. cow
3. c. keratin
4. giraffe
   (It's the tallest animal in the world.)
5. A male African lion has a thick mane.
6. Gnus would rather be around giraffes, because lions hunt gnus.

South American Rain Forest
Pages 16–17

1. Possible answers:
   A macaw uses its beak to move from branch to branch. It uses its beak to crack nuts, seeds, and snail shells.
2. No
3. d. all of these
4. macaw and howler monkey
5. No—because a jaguar is a good swimmer.
6. Baby sloths ride on their mother's belly.
   Baby monkeys ride on their mother's back.
7. It would be easier to see a macaw because it is so colorful.
8. A savanna has more grass and not as many trees. (or, A rain forest has more trees.)
9. male African lion (20 hours a day)

Animals of Australia
26–27 pages

1. d. Big reds live in the rain forest.
2. No (It is a marsupial.)
3. a. jellylike animals
4. clownfish
5. c. fish
6. b. crocodile
7. Possible answers:
   Sharks have no bones. Sharks have rubbery cartilage.
8. kangaroo and koala
9. Example answer:
   Both can wind their tail around an object to hold on.
10. Yes. Koalas have sharp toenails.

Animals of Southern Asia
Pages 34–35

1. Bengal tiger
2. No (Only the males have tusks.)
3. a. Pythons eat tree leaves.
4. It has a really big nose.
5. Man of the Forest
6. No. (It has a tail.)
7. b. driver
8. African elephants have much bigger ears than Asian elephants.
9. Jaguars have spots and tigers have stripes.
10. Africa, South America

Animals of North America
Pages 44–45

1. the plains
2. c. camp food
3. You can count the rings on its horns to see how many years old it is.
4. d. Alaska
5. puma, mountain lion, panther
6. b. dry scales
7. A bald eagle's wing is longer.
8. a plateau (An aerie is an eagle's nest.)
9. elephant — calves
   eagle — eaglets
   koala — joeys
   bear — cubs
10. Pythons wrap around and squeeze (or strangle) their prey. Rattlesnakes bite with fangs and inject venom.